Grey Rabbit's 1,2,3

Alan Baker

Kingfisher Books

Kingfisher Books, Grisewood & Dempsey Ltd,
Elsley House, 24-30 Great Titchfield Street,
London W1P 7AD

First published in 1994 by Kingfisher Books
2 4 6 8 10 9 7 5 3 1

BRITISH LIBRARY CATALOGUING
IN PUBLICATION DATA
A catalogue record for this book is available
from the British Library

ISBN 1 85697 180 5

Cover designed by Caroline Johnson
Phototypeset by Southern Positives and
Negatives (SPAN), Lingfield, Surrey
Printed in Singapore

One day Grey Rabbit
found some playdough.

He made one
wiggly,
squiggly

worm,

two
chattering,
nattering

toucans,

three
growling,
prowling

bears,

3

four happy, yappy

dogs,

five
freckled,
speckled

frogs,

six
sliding,
gliding

snakes,

seven
so slow

snails,

eight
rumpeting,
trumpeting

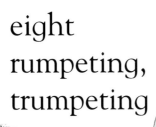

elephants,

nine
spotty,
dotty

bugs,

9

and ten
squeaking,
peeking

mice,

10

which left
at the end
of the day
one
weary,
bleary

rabbit fast asleep.